Upward, Inward, Outward Forward: Improving the 4 Dynamics of Your Cell Group

Revised Edition

Jim Egli

The Cell Group People™
A division of TOUCH® Outreach Ministries
Houston, Texas, U.S.A.

Published by Cell Group Resources™
P.O. Box 19888
Houston, Texas, 77224-9888, U.S.A.
(281) 497-7901 • Fax (281) 497-0904

Cover design by Don Bleyl
Text design by Rick Chandler
Editing by Scott Boren

International Standard Book Number: 1-880828-20-0

All Scripture quotations, unless otherwise indicated, are from the *Holy Bible*, New International Version, Copyright © 1973, 1978, 1984 by International Bible Society.
Used by permission.

The Cell Group People™ is a division of TOUCH® Outreach Ministries, a resource and consulting ministry for churches with a vision for cell-based local church structure.

To teach this workshop in your church, download the presentation from the TOUCH website with the username: "dynamics" and the password "growth". For detailed teaching instructions, purchase the *Cell Group Leader Training: Trainer's Guide.*

Find us on the World Wide Web at
http://www.cellgrouppeople.com or http://www.touchusa.org

Upward, Inward, Outward Forward: Improving the 4 Dynamics of Your Cell Group

Table of Contents

Introduction

Cells groups have captured the attention of Christian leaders around the world. We have known for some time that churches based on effective home groups are the fastest growing churches and are the most effective in reaching non-Christians with the Good News of Christ. Yet until recently no one had studied what makes cells or small groups grow. We did not know the answers to the simple question: Why do some groups thrive and grow while others struggle and stagnate?

Now our knowledge has dramatically changed. My friend, Joel Comiskey, statistically compared 700 small groups in seven different countries overseas. I took Joel's research tool and applied it to 200 groups in the United States. Joel's research overseas and mine in the U.S. revealed that the same dynamics make cells grow around the world.

As I applied these principles in my own church's cell ministry and taught them to others, I struggled with how to summarize and communicate these new discoveries. A breakthrough came when I realized that the concepts that Joel Comiskey uncovered could be communicated in four words. Growing cells groups practice four simple dynamics. They reach: Upward (in prayer), Inward (to experience community), Outward (to the lost), and Forward (in leadership multiplication).

Grasping these four principles and applying them rapidly accelerated the growth of my own cell group and transformed the way I equipped others. This new workshop is based on these simple but powerful principles.

The equipping in this workbook will inform and inspire you but it will go beyond that. Its six lessons will move you from learning to application as you pray and form a practical plan for your own group.

This leadership workshop is valuable for both current and future leaders. You can work through the six lessons and planning sessions in a full-day workshop or, alternately, in five weekly sessions.

At the end of the book, you will find an optional lesson in the Appendix that will help you integrate the four dynamics into the cell meeting.

I am excited about your potential and the potential of your group! Jesus has wonderful things in store for you. The four principles you will discover and apply are biblical, practical and proven. If you prayerfully reach Upward, Inward, Outward and Forward, you will see beautiful results.

Yours in Christ,
Jim Egli

Session

1

Capturing the
Cell Group Vision

Capturing the Cell Group Vision

 Personal Reflection

Write answers to the questions below. After you have written down your own responses, turn to someone near you and discuss your answers with one another.

- Have you ever experienced a life-changing small group? If so, when and where?

- Why did the group have so much of an impact on you?

- What did the leader do that made him or her effective as a leader?

Write your discoveries from the group discussion of the above questions below:

- What makes a group life-changing?

- What can leaders do to make their groups impact others' lives?

The Cell Group Vision:

The life appeared; we have seen it and testify to it, and we proclaim to you the eternal life, which was with the Father and has appeared to us. We proclaim to you what we have seen and heard, so that you also may have fellowship with us. And our fellowship is with the Father and with his Son, Jesus Christ.

- 1 John 1:2-3

Cell Life Involves:

• Experiencing the life of Christ . . .

• . . . in fellowship with one another

• Extending His life and fellowship to more and more people.

Cell Groups:

• Are the best way to unite discipleship, caring ministry, and evangelism.

• Have a support and training system to encourage their life and growth.

• Encourage each cell leader to receive a vision from God that fits within the overall cell group ministry of the church.

Cell Group Churches:

• Connect people through relationships.

• Form groups as the base of the church.

• Connect cell leaders to the church vision through coaches.

• Seek to grow and multiply groups by reaching unbelievers.

Cell Leaders:

- Follow Jesus, the Good Shepherd.

- Serve as under-shepherds.

- Normally oversee groups of no more than 15.

    - Even Jesus chose not to pastor a multitude of people.

    - 12 is the optimal number.

Cell Leader's Job Description:

1. To strengthen the weak.

2. To heal the sick.

3. To bind up the injured.

4. To bring back the strays and to seek the lost.

5. To lead gently and not harshly. (Ezekiel 34:1-6)

How Does Someone Become a Cell Leader?

1. Experience cell life through active involvement in a cell group.

2. Complete the church's required leadership training track.

3. Assist in a current group. (1 Timothy 3:10)

4. Receive the blessing of the church's pastoral leadership by demonstrating faithfulness to the Lord, the church's leadership and others.

 **Key Growth Factors**

Extensive statistical research has been done by Dr. Joel Comiskey and Jim Egli on what factors contribute to cell group growth. This research involved surveying 900 cell group leaders in the United States and seven other countries. It compared information about the groups' growth with their personal information and behavior.

In all eight countries the same factors impacted group growth.

Guess what they were.

Cell Group Leaders whose groups grow most rapidly . . .

Amount of Difference:	Big	Little	No
Are Married			
Are Single			
Are Well-educated			
Have an Outgoing Personality			
Are Younger			
Have Been a Christian a Long Time			
Have the Gift of Evangelism			
Have the Gift of Teaching			
Pray Daily for their Cell Members			
Spend More Time Daily with God			
Set Goals for Group Multiplication			
Identify and Involve New Leaders			
Spend More Time with Cell Members			
Follow Up on Visitors			
Spend More Time Preparing for the Cell Meeting			

Dynamic Cell Ministry Involves:

- Reaching Upward to God
- Reaching Inward to Build Body Life
- Reaching Outward to the Lost
- Moving Forward to Multiply Ministry

The three-legged stool.

1. Prayer is the central element through which all of the elements emerge. Our relationship with the Lord connects all of the dimensions and holds them all together.

2. We need all four elements or the stool will fall.

3. Without all four a cell is on a dead end street.

4. With all four working together there will be strength, life and growth.

Small Group Leadership Assessment

This form will help you assess the effectiveness of your small group ministry. Answer the questions by circling a number on each continuum showing where you or your group falls on each scale. After you have responded to the questions, follow the instructions at the end of the form to get your results.

Upward-Connecting Your Group to God:

How many days each week do you pray for the other members of your small group?

0 Days	1-2 Days	3-4 Days	5-6 Days	7 Days	
0	1	2	3	4	_____

How many minutes do you spend in devotional time with the Lord on the average day?

0-5	6-15	16-30	31-45	46+	
0	1	2	3	4	_____

How many minutes does your cell or small group spend in worship in its meetings?

0-4	5-9	10-14	15-19	20+	
0	1	2	3	4	_____

How many minutes does your group spend in prayer in its meetings?

0-5	6-15	16-30	31-45	46+	
0	1	2	3	4	_____

How often does your group see wonderful and miraculous answers to prayer?

Never	Sometimes	Often	Very Often	Regularly	
0	1	2	3	4	_____

Total: _____

Inward-Building Community:

How many times in the average four week span does your cell or small group meet?

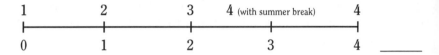

How many parties or fun activities has your group enjoyed together in the past three months?

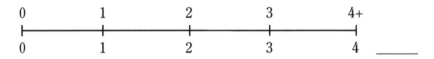

How many times have you invited group members to your home or a restaurant for a meal in the past two months?

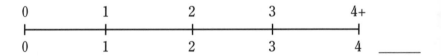

How often do most of your cell or small group members sit together in Sunday worship?

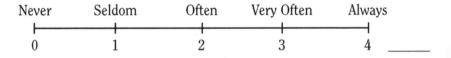

How often do you communicate with cell members by phone, email, cards or letters in order to encourage them?

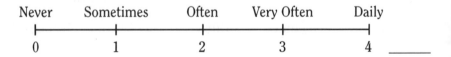

Total: _____

Outward-Reaching the Lost:

How often does your group take time in its meetings to pray for those that do not yet know Christ?

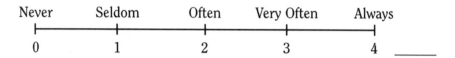

Never	Seldom	Often	Very Often	Always
0	1	2	3	4 ____

How many days each week do you pray for the salvation of unbelievers?

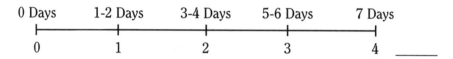

0 Days	1-2 Days	3-4 Days	5-6 Days	7 Days
0	1	2	3	4 ____

How many parties or fun events has your group done in the past three months that were targeted to appeal to non-Christians?

0	1	2	3	4+ ____

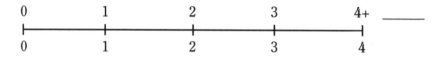

0	1	2	3	4

When a visitor attends your small group for the first time, how often are they followed up with a phone call, note or visit?

Never	Seldom	Often	Very Often	Always
0	1	2	3	4 ____

Does your group have a clear, dated goal for when it will multiply or give birth to a new group?

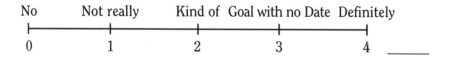

No	Not really	Kind of	Goal with no Date	Definitely
0	1	2	3	4 ____

Total: _____

Forward-Multiplying Leaders:

How many individuals or couples in your group serve as interns or assistants right now?

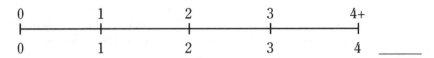

What percentage of your group members do you expect to lead a group at some point in the future?

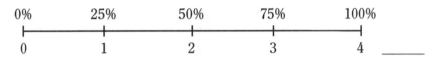

What percentage of the youth and adults in your group do you involve in leading parts of the cell meeting?

How often do your prayers for your cell include a prayer for the multiplication of leaders?

```
Never      Seldom       Often    Very Often      Always
├───────────┼────────────┼────────────┼────────────┤
0           1            2            3            4        _____
```

How many individuals or couples in your group do you expect to go through group leadership training in the next year?

Total: _____

Enter your totaled scores from each of the four parts as dots on the chart below and connect the dots.

#	Upward	Inward	Outward	Forward
20				
18				
16				
14				
12				
10				
8				
6				
4				
2				

Your lowest score shows your most critical area for improvement.
Scores below 10 are cause for alarm. Scores below seven indicate serious need. Prayerfully consider the results of this form as you plan your next steps throughout this workshop.

Small Group Leadership Assessment Summary Form:

Please complete this form and give a copy of it to your pastor for review.

What were your four scores?

Upward: _____

Inward: _____

Outward: _____

Forward: _____

Are you currently a cell or small group leader? Yes _____ No _____

If you are a group leader, please answer the questions below:

How many months have you led a group? _____ Months

Has your group multiplied since you became a leader? Yes _____ No _____

If so, how many times has it multiplied? _____

If so, how many months did it take to multiply? (Give an average if it has multiplied more than once.) _____ Months

Why Make Plans?

Commit to the Lord whatever you do, and your plans will succeed.

- Proverbs 16:3

- Good plans begin with a pure devotion to God.

- He reveals priorities.

- Without priorities, the "tyranny of the urgent" takes over.

- Cell groups grow when they focus on priorities not emergencies.

  - As one man said, "I had rather build a fence at the edge of a cliff than put an ambulance at the bottom."

- When you hear God's "Yes," you know when to say, "No."

  - Dr. Neighbour says, "For every, 'Yes,' there will be five, 'Nos.'"

Session

2

Reach Upward:
How to Plug into God's Power

How to Personally Plug into God's Power

Christ is Our Life Source!

I am the vine; you are the branches. If a man remains in me and I in him, he will bear much fruit; apart from me you can do nothing.

- Jesus (John 15:5)

- If we remain, we will bear much fruit!

This is to my Father's glory, that you bear much fruit, showing yourselves to be my disciples.

- Jesus (John 15:8)

- To "remain" means to "dwell, abide, or rest."

- Apart from Him, we can accomplish nothing. Ministry and leadership apart from Christ is like pushing a car that is out of gas, or using a mixer that is not plugged in!

- Listen and obey. Obedience, not activity, is the key.

 ## Ideas to Personally Plug into Christ

1. Take consistent time with Christ . . .

- Daily time. Take time every single day following the Seven-Minute Rule.

> The *Seven-Minute Rule*: Taking at least seven minutes each day with God for the rest of your life. It encourages every cell member in daily consistency.

- Generous time. If you are consistently taking daily time, begin taking a generous amount of time each day to enjoy God. You can determine what generous is for you right now in your life and walk with the Lord.

- Voluntary vulnerability. If you are stuck and cannot move forward, consider fasting. This means going without food to focus more on prayer. It makes you feel weak and vulnerable. It is a way to get serious about prayer without waiting for problems to make you feel weak and desperate.

2. Pray consistently for cell members. Statistical research by Joel Comiskey shows that cell leaders who pray for members six or seven days a week grow twice as fast as those who pray for members one or two days a week!

- Use prayer cards or a prayer journal.

- Pray for cell members with your cell intern or spouse.

3. Listen to God. As Jesus did, take time to listen to God as you pray for cell members.

- Luke 22:31-32

Personal Worksheet
Going Deeper with Christ

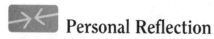 **Personal Reflection**

• How is God calling you to more fully abide in Christ?

• What obstacle or obstacles have kept you from time with God?
  Are there strongholds behind these obstacles that need to be dealt with
  or repented of? (For example, materialism or people-pleasing may be
  behind busyness.)

• What is one thing that you would like to do to pray more specifically
  for cell members? What is the next step in fulfilling this action?

After answering the questions above, share and pray with one or two
persons near you.

Ideas to Help You Plug into God's Power as a Group

1. Take a generous amount of time for prayer in group meetings.

   - Minimize other dimensions of the meeting. (Worship and teaching take place on Sunday morning, but corporate prayer and ministry are minimal in the large group setting.)

   - Divide into small groups, such as men and women, or groups of three or four to maximize personal sharing, prayer and ministry.

2. Have "Half-Nights of Prayer" every six to eight weeks. These consistently move groups to a deeper level in faith and expectancy.

   - You may need to schedule it on a night other than the cell meeting to allow it to go later.

   - You may invite cell members who want to join you in fasting for one or two meals proceeding the evening.

   - Two formats are given on page 25.

3. Practice prayer walking or driving to claim areas for God, seeking His mercy and inviting His Spirit to work in power.

4. Consider fasting to get things in gear. Involving group members in fasting for a specific need and period of time can move things off center, just as personal fasting can do.

5. Share how you are praying with cell members.

6. Keep a cell group prayer journal.

7. Make prayer visits to member's homes.

- 20-30 minutes in length.

- Ask for any prayer needs.

- Pray for needs.

- Share a word of encouragement.

- Pray for unbelieving friends.

8. Appoint an Upward Captain.

- Short-term role for a cell member who feels called to help the cell leader advance prayer in the group.

Samples:

Half-Night of Prayer Agenda 1

7:00 Praise and Worship
7:15 Silent Confession
7:20 Prayers of Thanksgiving
7:30 Announcements
7:40 Blessing & Prayer for each person/couple
8:50 Break
9:00 Pray over names from the group's Blessing (outreach) List
9:15 Pray for anointing to reach the lost
9:30 In groups, pray for the church, nation, world
9:50 Prayer of Dedication of our Cell
10:00 Refreshments and Fellowship

Half-Night of Prayer Agenda 2

Part 1: Private Reflection (30 minutes)
Have each member pray privately through Ps. 103.

Part 2: Worship (30 minutes)

Part 3: Discussion (20-30 minutes)
Read Luke 11:5-13
1. Do you view God as being like the sleeping man or like a good Father?
2. How would you describe the person in vs. 8 who is seeking the help?
3. When was the last time you were like this before God?
4. What is the result of the boldness in vs. 9-10?
5. What does it make you feel like to be bold before God?

Part 4: Concert prayer for five minutes in each of the following areas:
(60 minutes) Worship and Praise to God; Prayer for self; Prayer for family; Prayer for church and its leaders; Prayer for non-Christian friends; Prayer for your nation.

Break

Part 5: Prayer walk the neighborhood (30 minutes)

Part 6: Pray for one another (30 minutes)

Part 7: Pray over names from the group's Blessing List (30 minutes)

Part 8: Closing

Make a Plan to Plug into God's Power as a Group

Ask!

So I say to you: Ask and it will be given to you; seek and you will find; knock and the door will be opened to you. For everyone who asks receives; he who seeks finds; and to him who knocks, the door will be opened.

- Jesus (Luke 11:9-10)

Expect Miracles!

Did I not tell you that if you believed, you would see the glory of God?

- Jesus (John 11:40)

Pray and Plan with Others Now.

- Take time to pray, asking God to lead you and your group deeper into prayer. (If there are others at this meeting from your own group, do this exercise with them. If not, find one or two planning partners with whom you can do this and subsequent planning activities.)

- Write down two or three specific things that your group can do in the next two months to go deeper in prayer. Use the sample worksheet and blank worksheet on the following two pages as guides to help you make your plans specific and doable.

Sample Upward! Group Worksheet

This page is included as an example. Develop your own Upward! plan to connect your group to God using the blank planning page that follows.

Item	Dates	Who Will Do What
Half-Nights of Prayer	12/3, 7:00-10:00 p.m.	Todd will plan agenda. Vicki will arrange worship and childcare.
	2/5, 7:00-10:00 p.m.	Jim will plan worship & communion. - Will ask Ike to lead second hour - Will ask Laponza to lead worship - Jan will arrange childcare.
Women's Thursday prayer luncheon	Try every other week for two months	Vicki will set up date with Joanna and Eno.
Fasting for Evangelism	Every Tuesday between New Years and Easter of Next Year	Leaders will fast two meals and invite others to join them fasting one or two meals to focus prayer on the lost. Jim will begin publicity at the close of the first half-night of prayer. (12/3)

Upward! Group Worksheet

Develop a plan to deepen prayer in your cell. Work with others from your group. If you are alone, develop a working plan realizing that it will change as you confer with others from your cell.

Item	Dates	Who Will Do What

Important! When you have completed your worksheet, enter the dates on the planning calendar in the back of this booklet.

Session

3

Reach Inward:
Develop a Plan to Build
Community

Entering into Community

We proclaim to you what we have seen and heard, so that you also may have fellowship with us. And our fellowship is with the Father and with his Son, Jesus Christ.

- 1 John 1:3

Let the word of Christ dwell in you richly as you teach and admonish one another with all wisdom, and as you sing psalms, hymns and spiritual songs with gratitude in your hearts to God.

- Colossians 3:16

From him (Christ) the whole body, joined and held together by every supporting ligament, grows and builds itself up in love, as each part does its work.

- Ephesians 4:16

We Do Not Create Community, We Enter Into It!

(I pray) . . . that all of them may be one, Father, just as you are in me and I am in you.

- Jesus (John 17:21)

A Cell is . . .

- More than a once-a-week meeting.

- A "body" of believers experiencing community in Christ.

- A family-Caring for one another and extending Christ's love.

  - Not a perfect family
  - A healthy family
  - A healing family

The Stages of Group Life

1. **Forming.** This "honeymoon" stage is exciting. People are getting to know each other and are enjoying it.

2. **Storming.** In this "conflict" phase of cell life, personality and value differences create tension. People are getting to know each other better and often are not enjoying it!

3. **Norming.** Often called the "community" stage. In this phase of cell life, people have worked through many of their differences and are learning to love and appreciate one another. A sense of united vision moves the group forward.

4. **Performing.** Although outreach should be happening at every stage of cell life, it often accelerates at this point. For the group to remain intimate and effective you must multiply the group and leadership now. If you do not, the group will slowly lose vitality.

 ## To Cultivate Community:

• Model transparency, sharing your own needs.

• End meetings on time to allow for fellowship after the meeting.

• Open your home to others.

• Have fun and food together as a group.

• Include people in everyday activities of shopping, entertainment and serving one another.

• Sit together, if possible, at your church's worship services.

• Teach the stages of cell life to help people have realistic expectations.

• Phone one another between meetings.

• Encourage cell members to develop accountability relationships.

• Appoint an Inward Captain to help cultivate community.

Develop a Plan
to Build Community

 **Personal Reflection**

- What stage of cell life is your group in right now (forming, storming, norming or performing)?

- What relational needs are in your group now?

- What would you like to see happen in the next two or three months to deepen relationships in your group?

- Take a few moments to ask the Holy Spirit to build life-giving community in your group.

Make a plan to deepen community.

- Outline a possible plan to build community in your group on page 34.

Sample Inward! Group Worksheet

Develop a plan to enter community in your cell. If there are others from your group present at this meeting, work on this plan together.

Item	Dates	Who Will Do What
Game-night	12/3	John & Cindy will host. Terry will organize finger-foods.
Send notes of encouragement	Once per month	Cell Interns
Send email twice per month to all members with email, sharing upcoming events and prayer concerns.	Begin 12/10	Jim
Invite Smiths over for Dinner	12/14	George & Iris
Cell Christmas party & caroling	12/21	Todd & Jan
Birthday cake at cell meeting for Terry	1/14	Theresa will bring cake.
Help Smiths move	1/30	John will coordinate

Important! When you have completed your worksheet, enter the dates on the same planning calendar that you began earlier in this training.

Inward! Group Worksheet

Develop a plan to enter community in your cell. Work with others from your group. If you are alone, develop a working plan realizing that it will change as you confer with others from your cell.

Item	Dates	Who Will Do What

Important! When you have completed your worksheet, enter the dates on the planning calendar in the back of this booklet.

Session

4

Reach Outward:
Making a Plan to
Mobilize Outreach

Effective Evangelism

 Personal Reflection

Answer the questions on this page by yourself.

1. When you hear the word "evangelism," which of the following words or images immediately come to your mind? (Check all that apply).
   - _____ 1. Door-to-door witnessing
   - _____ 2. Passing out tracts on the street
   - _____ 3. Revival or tent meetings
   - _____ 4. Billy Graham
   - _____ 5. Caring friendship
   - _____ 6. Sunday evening services
   - _____ 7. Prayer
   - _____ 8. Talking
   - _____ 9. Listening

2. When you think of your own life, who was most influential in your decision to follow Christ?
   - _____ 1. Friend
   - _____ 2. Relative
   - _____ 3. Pastor
   - _____ 4. Co-worker or classmate
   - _____ 5. Stranger
   - _____ 6. Other: _____

3. Which of the following words describe how you were influenced to Christ:
   - _____ 1. Warmth
   - _____ 2. Put-down
   - _____ 3. Cared for
   - _____ 4. Loving
   - _____ 5. Insensitive
   - _____ 6. Listened to
   - _____ 7. Manipulated
   - _____ 8. Other: _____
   - _____ 9. Other: _____

4. How many times did you hear the Gospel before you said "yes" to Christ?
_____

5. Did you make one total commitment to Christ, or was it a series of commitments, setbacks and recommitments?

6. How long did the process take? _____

7. How many people were involved in influencing you to receive Christ? _____

When you have completed your answers, discuss them quickly with someone near you.

Discoveries About
Effective Evangelism

Experience Reveals:

1. Many people have inaccurate mental pictures of evangelism.

   a. They feel nervous or guilty when they think about "evangelism."

   b. Yet almost all Christians feel good about the way they themselves were evangelized!

2. The best evangelists are ordinary Christians.

3. Active love is primary in drawing others to Christ.

4. Evangelism takes time!

5. Multiple people are usually involved.

6. The questions we just used can help your own cell members get a positive and accurate understanding of evangelism.

7. Other insights?

Biblical Images of Evangelism

1. The Friendship Image

People in Scripture were often brought to Christ through friends
or relatives.
- Andrew brought Peter to Christ. (John 1:40-41)
- Matthew brought his pagan co-workers and friends. (Matthew 9:10)
- Cornelius influenced relatives and fellow soldiers to receive Christ.
  (Acts (10:22-24)
- Lydia and the Philippian jailer brought their families to Christ. (Acts 16)
- Scripture gives many other examples.

2. The Sowing and Reaping Image

- "One sows and another reaps." Jesus (John 4:37)
- Evangelism takes time.
- It is a process.
- It often involves multiple people.

Ideas to Enhance Outreach Efforts

1. Be Visitor Friendly!

- If possible, move the cell from home to home to make it easier to invite friends.

- When there are visitors:

  - Explain everything.

  - Use song sheets.

  - Follow-up on visitors and let them know where you are meeting next week.

2. Keep Outreach Central

- Consistently "Share the Vision" in cell for outreach and multiplication.

- Make the Witness portion of your meeting first on the agenda if needed.

- Get people trained in relational evangelism.

3 Write a Mission Statement

- Is there a certain group of people or part of town that God has called your cell to reach out to?

- What do you want people who become involved in your group to experience?

- Write a simple mission statement that expresses the purpose of your group. (For example: The Bear Creek Cell's mission is to reach an expanding number of families and individuals in west Houston and Katy bringing them into a life-changing relationship with God and each other.)

- Review this mission statement often in your cell meetings so that you remain focused on God's purpose for your group.

4. Set Simple Goals

- How many people do you want to see come to Christ through the influence of your group in the next nine months?

- When would you like to multiply your cell group or launch a new group out of your existing group?

5. Utilize The Blessing List

Step 1: Prepare

- Photocopy the "Identifying Your Circle of Influence" master (one for each cell member).

- Complete it yourself.

Step 2: Present

- Distribute "Identifying Your Circle of Influence."

- Have each member write the names of unbelieving friends, co-workers, fellow students and neighbors.

- Have each person circle the names of their two friends who are probably most open to Christ.

Step 3: Make a Master List

- Put the two names from each list on the large "Our Blessing List."

- Have each member record the group's blessing list on the bottom of their page.

Step 4: Pray!

- Encourage each member to pray regularly for their own list and the group's list.

- Pray God's blessing and work in the lives of the group list in your weekly cell meetings.

- Love and serve these persons, individually and as a group.

Personal Reflection

- Is your group currently using a Blessing List?

- If "yes," how could you use it more consistently and effectively?

- If "no," write down on your planning calendar when you should introduce the list and begin using it. Before that date, enter a reminder to photocopy the necessary "Identifying Your Circle of Influence" page from the Blessing List tool.

6. Cooperate with God

- Are there adults or children close to your group or its members who seem open to God right now? If so, write their names below.

- Are there new Christians in your group with unsaved friends or relatives your group should reach?

7. Party! (Use food and fun to reach out and build relationships!)

• What birthdays or holidays are coming up that would be natural times to reach out and socially include non-Christian friends, neighbors or coworkers in a fun activity?

• What are some of the interests of non-Christians in your cell's circle of influence? Do they like to bowl, eat, watch or compete in sports, etc.?

• After reviewing your answers to the above two questions, should you change the social activities your cell has planned so that non-Christians can be more easily included? Put these on your calendar.

8. Tie into Church-wide Harvest Events

- Are there Christian concerts, performances or other entertaining events taking place in your church or community that cell members could invite unbelieving friends to attend?

- Write these events on your planning calendar. Then write down a reminder five weeks ahead of the event to pray for these events and to encourage cell members to invite receptive friends to them.

9. Appoint an Outward Captain

- Who in the group has a passion to build relationships with unbelievers and reach out to the lost?

- Is this person willing to help the cell leader advance the Outward movement of the group?

Planning

Outward! Group Worksheet

Develop a plan for outreach in your cell. Work with others from your group. If you are alone, develop a working plan realizing that it will change as you confer with others from your cell.

Item	Dates	Who Will Do What

Important! When you have completed your worksheet, enter the dates on the planning calendar in the back of this booklet.

Session

5

Move Forward:
How to Multiply Your Ministry

Multiply Yourself

And the things you have heard me say in the presence of many witnesses entrust to reliable men (Original Greek: persons) who will also be qualified to teach others.

- Paul (2 Timothy 2:2)

Follow my example, as I follow the example of Christ.

- Paul (1 Corinthians11:1)

 Ideas to Multiply Yourself!

1. Pray! (Matthew 9:38)

2. See everyone as a future leader. (Ask God for faith to see the incredible potential in others.)

3. Constantly involve others during the cell meeting and other ministry opportunities.

4. Give people responsibilities BEFORE you ask them to be leaders.

5. Consult with those over you before giving any titles or positions.

6. Pray and plan with your interns.

7. Ask questions before you correct during debriefing session. (James 1:19) i.e. "What did you think about the meeting? What would you do differently?"

8. Encourage! Interns need more encouragement than correction. Apply the 4 to 1 rule: 4 times more encouragement than correction.

9. Send people to the next cell training.

Give your group away!

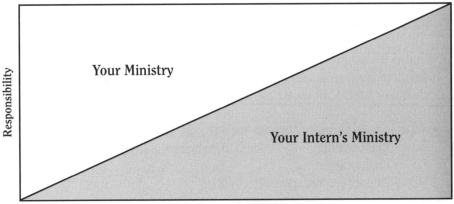

Responsibility

Your Ministry

Your Intern's Ministry

First 6 Months of Cell Cycle

Multiply Your Group!

1. Multiplication Methods:

- **Multiply.** Two groups of similar size multiply from parent group.
- **Launch.** Core group from parent group launches a new group.
- **Cooperative Launch.** One or more from your group joins one or more from other groups to launch a new cell.
- **Plant.** One person from parent group plants a new group and often remains a part of the parent group.

2. Multiplication Principles:

- Keep the vision of multiplication continually before the group right from the beginning.

- Concentrate on multiplying leaders, not just new groups.

- Lead group members to pray often, asking God if He would use them in birthing a new cell. Help members answer God's call and destiny for their lives.

- New groups are birthed by sending out a prepared leader or by the current cell leader starting a new group.

- Protect the sense of community group members have developed. It does not have to be sacrificed for multiplication to occur.

Personal Reflection

Prayerfully respond to the following:

1. What is it that prevents me from becoming a future cell leader? (For those who already serve as cell leaders: what is it that prevents me from being the cell leader I feel God wants me to be?)

   • Your answer(s) might include such things as:
   - Lack of time   - Unconfessed sin in my life
   - Lack of training   - Don't want to
   - Uncooperative spouse   - Etc.

   • List your answer(s) here:

2. Are you willing to allow God to begin dealing with the item(s) you listed in #1 above?
   _____ Yes
   _____ No
   _____ Maybe, I'll pray about it

3. If your answer to #2 is "Yes," who is it that you will ask to offer you prayer, support, and accountability as you allow God to work a transformation in your life?

   Write name here: _____

   Write when and how you will contact this person to ask for their help here: _____

   _____

   Record information on the planning calendar at the back of this booklet.

4. Whether or not you feel led to be in leadership, are you willing to ask God whether you should be a part of a newly birthed cell group or not?

5. Are you willing to share your answers to the above questions with your planning group when you meet in a few minutes?

_____ Yes

_____ No, I'd rather not

(It's ok and even important to be open and honest with each other in these matters.)

Sample Forward! Group Worksheet

List Names of Group Members*	**	Previous Experience and Strengths	Next Steps in Leadership
(Jim)		Wants to be a leader as soon as possible.	Needs to learn how to relate to unbelievers.
Diane	√	Loves to talk with unbelievers. Very good learner.	Seek more flexible work schedule.
(Judy)	√	Very social. Has led worship effectively.	Should attend the next cell leader training.
Ben		Very new Christian but willing to learn.	Allow God to work through some personal issues.

* Circle those who are interested in becoming a cell group leader in the futu:
** Make a check in this column to mark people who are willing to pray abou participation in a future cell group birthing.
† When you have completed your worksheet, enter the dates on the planning calendar in the back of this booklet.

Tasks to Assign Them	What Kind of Help is Needed from the Group	Goal Date [†]	Done
y for lost friends. ganize the next cell ty to reach out to ends.	Hang out with unbelieving friends of other cell group members.	April 10	
ganize the prayer iin. id icebreaker.	Prayer that boss will allow her to change her hours.	?	
id the Word portion the meeting.	Pray that husband will allow her to become a leader.	April 15	
eet with cell leader to cuss issues that hold n back.	Encouragement	June 1	

Forward! Group Worksheet

List Names of Group Members*	**	Previous Experience and Strengths	Next Steps in Leaders

* Circle those who are interested in becoming a cell group leader in the futu:

**Make a check in this column to mark people who are willing to pray about participation in a future cell group birthing.

† When you have completed your worksheet, enter the dates on the planning calendar in the back of this booklet.

Tasks to Assign Them	What Kind of Help is Needed from the Group	Goal Date[†]	Done

Session

6

Putting Your Plans into Action

Refine Your Plans

God Says to Refine Your Plans with Others

For lack of guidance a nation falls, but many advisers make victory sure.
- Proverbs 11:14

Plans fail for lack of counsel, but with many advisers they succeed.
- Proverbs 15:22

Make plans by seeking advice; if you wage war, obtain guidance.
- Proverbs 20:18

 ## Who Can Help Shape Your Plans?

1. Your leader, intern, spouse or other interested cell members.

2. You can use the worksheets and/or calendar as starting points.

3. Your cell coach or pastor.

- They will be impressed by your work!

- They know of church events and other important considerations.

- Your leader should at least initial your cell plans.

4. Cell members should help plan individual parties and outreach events.

Next Steps

Refine Your Plans.

- What individuals do you need to confer with to finalize these plans?

- When should you make appointments to meet with them? (Write down tentative times on your planning calendar).

 Personal Reflection

- What two events that you planned today are most important?

- What are the next steps in implementing these activities or events? (Enter these next steps on the calendar.)

- What is one thing that you sense God saying to you today?

- What would you most like prayer for as you consider your cell group today?

Discuss Your Answers and Pray!

- Take time now to discuss your responses to the above questions and to pray together.

- From the discussion above, enter the key action items on your calendar.

Appendix

A

The Four Dynamics in the Cell Meeting

Moving Upward, Inward, Outward and Forward in Your Cell Meeting

A Recommended Cell Meeting Format for a 90 Minute Meeting:

Portion of Meeting	Explanation	Flow
Welcome • 10 Minutes	Easy to answer icebreaker question that invites involvement from everyone.	You to Me
Worship • 15 Minutes	Simple worship that focuses on the Lord.	Us to God
Word • 25 Minutes of Study • 25 Minutes of Prayer	Interaction and application of God's Word, followed by ministry to one another.	God to Us
Witness • 15 Minutes	Planning and Prayer for Outreach.	God Through Us

Tips:
- Vary the format of the meeting. Do not get into a rut.
- Delegate different parts of the meeting. This leads the group Forward.
- Use food.
- Flow naturally in and out of the meeting.
  - In other words, do not say, "For our icebreaker tonight . . ."
  - Just discuss the topics without making the meeting feel official.
- End the meeting on time.
- Relax.
- Be Personal.

Follow These Simple Principles:

Welcome
- Use non-threatening questions that can be easily answered.
- Go in a circle.
- Whoever asks the question answers it first.
- Example: "What is your favorite food and when did you last eat it?"
- Old Stand-by: "What has been the most significant thing about your week?"

Worship
- Use simple songs normally sung in your church.
- Do not try to reproduce large group worship.
- Prepare song sheets.
- Be creative.

Word
- Facilitate discussion; do not teach.
- Ask open-ended questions.
    - Not: "What did Peter do to deny Christ?"
    - Rather: "What do you do when you are in a situation like Peter's?"
- Encourage and model vulnerability.
- Allow plenty of time for prayer and responding to God.
- Simple questions to ask:
    1. What stands out to you in this passage?
    2. What seems to be the main point?
    3. Can you illustrate this truth from an experience in your life?
    4. What is God saying to you right now?

Witness
- Plan outreach events.
- Prayer for those listed on your Blessing List.
- Discuss ministry needs of non-Christian friends.
- Cast vision for multiplication.

Improving Your Cell Group Meeting

Pray together with others from your cell group or church. Then discuss the following questions:

1. **Upward:** What can you do to improve worship and prayer in your cell group?

2. **Inward:** What can you do to deepen the level of intimacy and sharing?

3. **Outward:** How can you make outreach more central to your group and your meeting?

4. **Forward:** What can you do to involve more people in the leadership of your meeting?

Appendix

B

Calendars

Month	Sunday	Monday	Tuesday	Wednesday	Thursday	Friday	Saturday
#1 Year: Month: Review these plans with your cell coach or pastor to get his or her ideas and approval. Have them initial each page of your plan.							

Month	Sunday	Monday	Tuesday	Wednesday	Thursday	Friday	Saturday
#2 Year: Month: Review these plans with your cell coach or pastor to get his or her ideas and approval. Have them initial each page of your plan.							

Month	Sunday	Monday	Tuesday	Wednesday	Thursday	Friday	Saturday
#3 Year: Month: Review these plans with your cell coach or pastor to get his or her ideas and approval. Have them initial each page of your plan.							

Month	Sunday	Monday	Tuesday	Wednesday	Thursday	Friday	Saturday
#4 Year: Month: Review these plans with your cell coach or pastor to get his or her ideas and approval. Have them initial each page of your plan.							

Notes

Notes

Notes